Get Set Go Phonics

Little Red Riding Hood

Phonics Consultant Susan Purcell

Illustrator Monika Filipina

Concept Fran Bromage

Miles Kelly

Once upon a time, there was a little girl who wore a red skirt, red shoes and a red hood. Her name was Little Red Riding Hood.

Say the words as you spot things beginning with the r sound in the picture.

red

rabbit

roof

One day her mother said, "Grandma is really not well. Can you run round to see her right away?"

Spot the word that doesn't begin with the r sound.

rat   nice   ring   room

Emphasize the w sound (as in wood)

Red Riding Hood walked through the wood to Grandma's house. A wolf was waiting for her to wander closer – then he jumped out!

Sound out these words with the w sound.

way   win   wig   wool

well   wasp   web

"Well, hello," growled the wolf, "do you want to play?"

"No, thank you. I'm walking to Grandma's house," said Red Riding Hood, looking worried.

Spot the word that doesn't begin with the w sound.

week   wash   worm   very

"Before you leave the wood, why not pick some flowers?" said the wolf.
"I should! What a good idea," said Red Riding Hood.

Spot the word that doesn't use the oo sound.

boat   could   foot   look

"What a treasure you are!" said the wolf. "It's a pleasure to meet you," and off he ran.

Sound out these words, which all use the zh sound.

measure   leisure   television

casual   usual

But that naughty wolf was soon knocking at Grandma's door. Grandma knew it was not Red Riding Hood, so she hid in the wardrobe.

Sound out these words with the n sound in different positions.

neck   noon   knot   gnaw

funny   line   pan   corn

When the wolf walked in,
Grandma was nowhere to
be seen. He put on her
nightgown and nightcap.

Spot the word that doesn't begin with the n sound.

nest   mint   knee   gnome

As you read, focus on the **or** sound (as in sort)

As the wolf got into bed, Red Riding Hood knocked on the door.

Straight away she saw something wasn't right.

Point to the d**oor** and then the wolf's p**aw**

Sound out these words, which all use the **or** sound.

sort **born** **horse**

jaw **straw** **autumn**

"Poor Grandma!" she said, your face looks very odd!"

Spot the word that doesn't use the **or** sound.

park   short   yawn   saucer

Emphasize the ear sound (as in dear)

"Hello, my dear," said the wolf. "Do not fear. Come and sit near me!"

Emphasize the ear sound as you say this sentence together.

"What big ears you have, Grandma!"
"All the better to hear you with."

"My, what big **eyes** you have, Grandma," said Red Riding Hood.

"All the better to see you with," repl**ie**d the sly wolf.

Try to focus on the **ie** sound (as in pie)

Sound out these words with the ie sound.

cry   fly   dry   tie   pie

ride   time   high   night

Highlight the ee sound (as in teeth)

"And your teeth are huge!" gasped Little Red Riding Hood.

"All the better to eat you with!" said the wolf, jumping to his feet.

Red Riding Hood screamed!

Sound out these words with the **ee** sound.

need   geese   tree   sweet
bead   treat   steam

The wolf threw off the nightdress and Red Riding Hood ran away as fast as she could, fearing for her life.

Say the words as you spot things with an f sound in the picture.

face

fingers

wolf

Draw attention to the h sound (as in his)

A woodcutter heard Red Riding Hood screaming. He rushed in holding his axe.

"I'll have that wolf's tail!" he hollered.

Say the names of the things with the h sound, as you spot them.

hood   hand   head

hedge   handle

Highlight
the ai sound
(as in tail)

But the big grey wolf
escaped with his tail.
He ran away and never
came near Red Riding
Hood again – hooray!

Spot the word that doesn't use the ai sound.

play   flat   rain   paint

17

Then Grandma groaned from inside the wardrobe.

The woodcutter grabbed the handle and let Grandma out.

Sound out some words that begin with the gr blend.

grip   gravy   growl   greedy

grill   group   grass

"Thank you!" said Grandma, grinning at the woodcutter, and grabbing Red Riding Hood for a great big hug.

Can you grin like Grandma?

Spot the word that doesn't use the **gr** sound.

pram   grow   green   grand

Sound out these words, which all use the k sound made by c and k.

cut   cow   card   castle

kiss   key   kitten

20

"This is cause for cake and a cup of coffee!" said Grandma, and went into the kitchen to put the kettle on, and fetch some cupcakes.

Say the words as you spot things with a k sound in the picture.

cake stand

cupcake

cup

Focus on the
kw blend
(as in quiet)

The wolf had had quite enough for one day. He went to live a quiet life deep in the wood and quivered and quaked whenever he saw Red Riding Hood!

Spot the word that doesn't begin with qu.

quit   queen   gust   quick

Ask your child to **retell** the story using
these key sounds and story images.

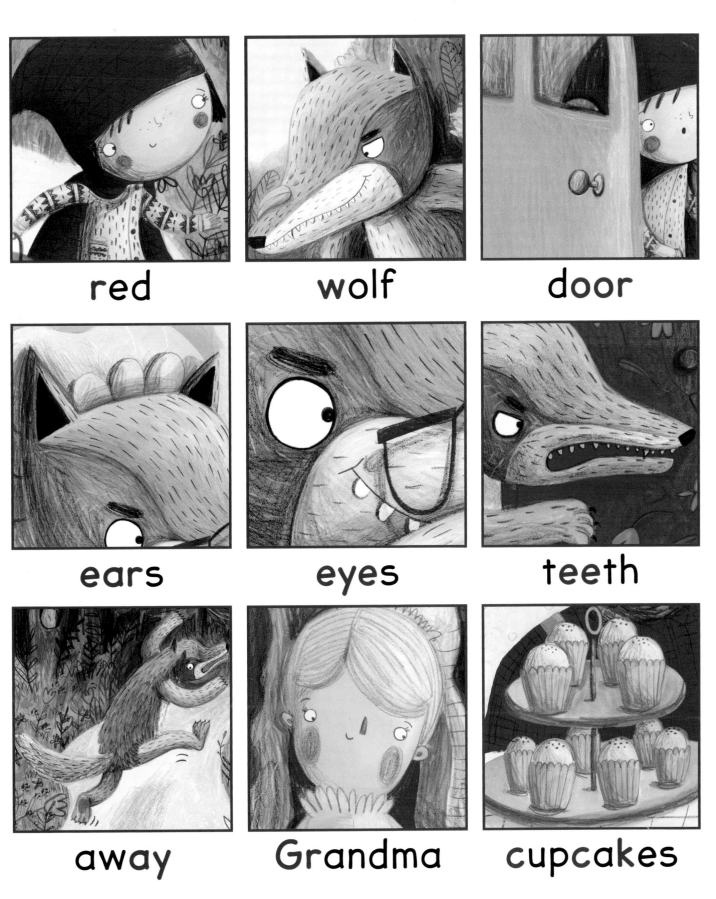

red

wolf

door

ears

eyes

teeth

away

Grandma

cupcakes

Say the words in each line out loud together.
Can you think of another word that uses the highlighted sound?

good   could   foot   book

usual   casual   leisure   measure

knew   nightcap   knock   gnome

saw   autumn   door   horse

eye   high   fly   pie   time

feet   treat   bead   sleep

face   life   wolf   fast

his   hedge   have   hand

quick   queen   quit   quiver

You've had fun with phonics! Well done.